Specials!

Ethics and moral issues

Christine Moorcroft

Acknowledgements

p23 *In and Out of Court* by Nigel Thomson. Reproduced with permission of Dunedin Academic Press.
p45 NMPFT/Science & Society Picture Library.

United Kingdom: Folens Publishers, Apex Business Centre, Boscombe Road, Dunstable, LU5 4RL.
Email: folens@folens.com

Ireland: Folens Publishers, Greenhills Road, Tallaght, Dublin 24.
Email: info@folens.ie

Poland: JUKA, ul. Renesansowa 38, Warsaw 01-905

Editor: Joanne Mitchell   Layout artist: Book Matrix
Cover design: Holbrook Design   Cover image: Corbis
Illustrations: Nigel Chilvers p52 (middle left); Peter Wilks of SGA pp6, 7, 8, 14, 26, 27, 36, 37, 38, 42, 46, 49, 51, 52, 56, 57, 60, 63

First published 2006 by Folens Limited.

British Library Cataloguing in Publication Data. A catalogue record for this publication is available from the British Library.

ISBN 1 84303 886 2 / 978 1 84303 886 3

Contents

Introduction

Specials! RE Ethics and moral issues provides ten units of work to help students with lower reading abilities to have access to the RE curriculum. Each unit is linked to the QCA scheme of work and to the 5–14 guidelines for RE.

It focuses on issues which can have a spiritual nature and draws on what the students learn from different religions. It also provides opportunities to consider Humanism.

The activities are intended for students whose reading comprehension age is between six and nine. Some student pages are more challenging than others; teachers will need to select accordingly.

Each unit contains four to six photocopiable activity sheets. Some of these are pages which provide background information or sources, such as newspaper articles, stories and factfiles, and should be used together with another activity sheet. They can be used in different ways, for example, students could work from them individually, in pairs or in small groups. Where necessary, vocabulary is provided on the activity sheet.

The **Teacher's notes** provide a small section of background information which gives guidance to the teacher when using **Activity sheets**. Also included in the Teacher's notes are:
- **Objectives** (the main skills and knowledge to be learned)
- **Prior knowledge** expected of students to be familiar with already in order to complete the activity sheets.
- **QCA links**
- **Scottish attainment targets**
- **Starter activities** introducing each unit or relating it to a previous topic.
- Suggestions about using the **Activity sheets**
- **Plenary session** which can be undertaken to recall key points.

At the end of the book is an **Assessment sheet** to help teachers to monitor students' progress and to provide a useful self-assessment record for the students. They could complete this individually, with the teacher also completing a copy; they can then compare and discuss the two. Alternatively, the students could work in pairs on peer assessments and then compare the outcomes with one another. The assessment sheet can be used to encourage the students to discuss their own progress, consider different points of view and, with guidance, to set targets.

Specials! RE Ethics and moral issues

Teacher's notes

Right and wrong

Objectives

- Know about some ways in which religious beliefs affect people's actions
- Know about some ways in which scriptures affect the lives of believers

Prior knowledge

The students should show some knowledge about the beliefs of Buddhists, Christians, Hindus, Jews, Muslims and Sikhs. They should be given opportunities to discuss the rules followed by people of these religions.

QCA links

Unit *8C* Beliefs and practice and *9C* Why do we suffer?

Scottish attainment targets

Other world religions
Strand – Moral values and attitudes
Level C/E

Background

The Buddhist code of conduct is the Eightfold Path. In addition to those listed on 'Doing right in Buddhism', it includes Right seeing (understanding the Four Noble Truths), Right effort (a sincere effort to follow the Eightfold Path) and Right contemplation (learning reflection and meditation). The Five Precepts provide rules for living – not to: kill or harm living things, steal, commit adultery, lie, drink alcohol or take drugs. In Hinduism, there are equivalent rules. Hindus worship God in the form of many gods and goddesses; they believe in reincarnation and that the better the life they live, the better their reincarnation. They practise Ahimsa (non-violence) and are forbidden to eat the meat of cows. In addition to following the Five Pillars of Islam, Muslims are required to observe rules for conduct set out in the Qur'an: worship only God, do not worship idols, avoid bribery, dishonesty, alcohol, forgery, gambling, gossiping, hoarding, murder, suicide, slandering, theft, damaging property and cruelty to animals. They are forbidden to eat pigs and are required to pay 2.5% of their wealth as a welfare due. In family life, they are encouraged to marry and to treat their parents with respect. They are required to dress modestly (usually interpreted to mean that men cover their bodies from the waist to knees and women cover all but the face and hands). Sikhs worship one god; they believe that everyone is equal and that all religions are worthy of respect. They are forbidden to steal, gamble, drink alcohol or take drugs (except as medicine). They should make an honest living by lawful work.

Starter activity

Together, read newspaper reports about robbery, assault, murder, rape, debt, disorderly behaviour and so on. Challenge the students to find reports about good deeds. Ask them to suggest rules people could follow in order to live a good life. List their responses on the flip chart.

Activity sheets

'Making a choice'. Ask the students to discuss, in pairs, the factors which might affect the answers given by the boy and girl in the picture. What would be the right response? What might stop them making this response?

'What is right?' Ask the students if they behave in the same way in all situations. What factors affect their behaviour? When they have completed the activity sheet, invite feedback and discuss.

'Doing right in Buddhism' lists five of the requirements of the Eightfold Path of Buddhism. Ask the students to give an example of an action for each requirement.

'What is wrong?' Ask the students to read the actions on the cards, cut them out and place them on the ladder in order, starting with the worst action at the top. They must justify where they have placed the cards. Once the ladder has been completed, ask them to discuss it as a group and to agree on any changes. Invite feedback from each group.

'Religious rights and wrongs'. The students should work in groups of four. Ask them to read the Ten Commandments and allocate one of the four religions listed on the chart to each student in each group. Help them to find out about the rules believers are expected to follow. What similarities can they find between all religions? They should fill in the chart.

Plenary

Explain that all religious believers have some kind of code of conduct to guide them and that there are similarities between these codes.

Activity sheet – Right and wrong

Making a choice

☞ Look at the picture and imagine you are approaching the bench where people your age are drinking alcohol.

What would affect your choice?

Discuss with a partner.

| If you say yes | ← |

| If you say no | ← |

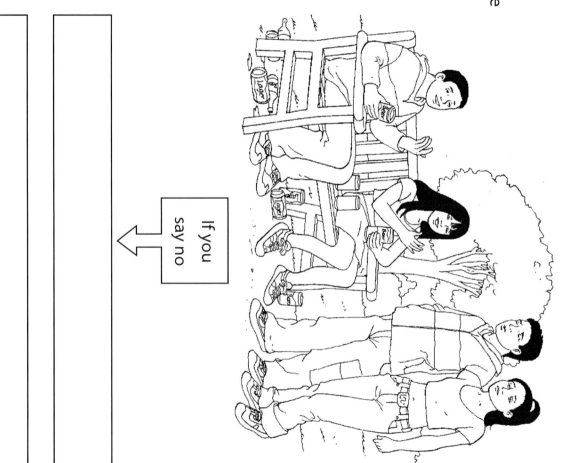

RE Ethics and moral issues

© Folens (copiable page)

Activity sheet – Right and wrong

What is right?

☞ What does it mean to do what is right?
List some good things to do.

Think of positive things. Try not to use the words 'Do not...'

At home	At school	With your friends	On buses or trains	In shops

☞ Make a list of situations when it is difficult to do what you know is right.
What makes this difficult?

Situation	Difficulty in doing what is right

Doing right in Buddhism

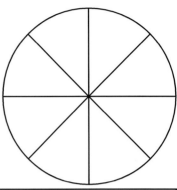

☞ In Buddhism, the Eightfold Path says what people should do.
The chart lists five actions from the Eightfold Path.
Give some examples which you could do.

Eightfold Path	Example
Right thought: pure thoughts with no selfishness or unkindness.	
Right speech: speaking the truth, with no gossip or talk which might encourage hatred or conflict.	
Right action: actions must not distress others or cause offence.	
Right livelihood: earning a living in a way which follows the Eightfold Path.	
Right mindfulness: being aware of and thinking about the activities of the body, voice and mind.	

Activity sheet – Right and wrong

What is wrong?

☞ A group of students listed actions they thought were wrong. They chose 10 and wrote them on the cards below.
Write four others of your own.
Put the wrong actions in order on the ladder with the worst at the top.

✂

Stealing	Swearing
Punching someone	Spitting at someone
Murder	Kicking someone
Harming an animal	Spreading unkind rumours
Making racist comments	Vandalism

1. _____

2. _____

3. _____

4. _____

5. _____

6. _____

7. _____

8. _____

9. _____

10. _____

11. _____

12. _____

13. _____

14. _____

Activity sheet – Right and wrong

Religious rights and wrongs

Christians and Jews follow the Ten Commandments.

☞ Work in a group of four.

☞ Each find out about the rules of another religion.
On a separate piece of paper, write notes about the rules of the religion you choose.

☞ Which of the Ten Commandments are also followed by that religion?
Fill in the chart by adding a tick or a cross.

Commandment	Buddhism	Christianity	Hinduism	Islam	Sikhism
You shall have no other gods.					
You shall not worship graven images.					
You shall not misuse the name of the Lord your God.					
Remember the Sabbath day and keep it holy.					
Honour your father and your mother.					
You shall not murder.					
You shall not commit adultery.					
You shall not steal.					
You shall not give false witness against your neighbour.					
You shall not covet your neighbour's possession.					

RE Ethics and moral issues   © Folens (copiable page)

Teacher's notes

Rules and laws

Objectives

- Know about some ways in which religious beliefs affect people's actions
- Know about some ways in which scriptures affect the lives of believers

Prior knowledge

The students should show some knowledge about the beliefs of Buddhists, Christians, Hindus, Jews, Muslims and Sikhs. They should be given opportunities to discuss the rules followed by people of these religions.

QCA link

Unit 8C Beliefs and practice

Scottish attainment targets

Personal search
Strand – Relationships and moral values
Level C/E

Background

Most religions set out a code of conduct or a set of rules for their adherents to follow. Most of them are believed to have been given by God to a key figure and handed down from one generation to the next. Christianity and Judaism have the Ten Commandments (given by God to Moses). In addition to this, Judaism has the Torah – a detailed set of rules about most aspects of life – which was written more than 4000 years ago and based on the laws given to Moses. Rabbis and other Jewish scholars interpret these for ordinary believers and answer their queries about how they apply to modern life. In Christianity, the two Great Commandments of Jesus are given the greatest importance (Love the Lord God with all your heart, with all your mind and with all your strength. Love your neighbour as you love yourself.). Throughout the Qur'an are rules and advice for Muslims. In Hinduism, there is no equivalent to the Ten Commandments, but the Law of Manu is considered to be the guide. Sikhism is a belief system developed from Hinduism by Guru Nanak and his followers; the main rule they added to those of Hinduism is that everyone is equal. Sikhism also has a set of symbolic rules set out by Guru Gobind Singh (the wearing of the Five Ks and the adoption of the names 'Singh' for males and 'Kaur' for females). Buddhism has the Eightfold Path – the result of the Buddha's enlightenment.

Starter activity

Ask the students to think of rules or laws which are frequently broken. Ask them, 'Why do people break rules or laws?'

Activity sheets

'Rules for reasons'. Ask the students about situations where they follow special rules, for example, at a swimming pool, at a club they belong to, or playing a game. Draw out that they probably do not follow a set of written or formally agreed rules but that there are certain things they would and would not do which show that they follow some kind of code of conduct. Ask the students which rules on the activity sheet they think are good rules and which are not. What makes a rule good?

'Your rules'. Ask the students to consider what they would do in each situation listed. Invite feedback. They should complete the chart.

'Lawbreakers'. Ask the students how the youngsters might feel about their punishments. Ask them to consider the different people affected by a crime committed by one person, and how they are affected. Were the punishments fair?

'Religious laws'. Remind the students about the rules and laws set down by some religions. Point out that some of these are similar to the laws of the land and that it would be a crime to disobey them, but that others are not connected with crime, for example, Buddhists do not kill animals for food; Sikhs must not cut their hair. Each student should research a different religious law and report back to the others.

'Lawmakers' encourages the students to consider the consequences of their actions. Begin with the example of making a lot of expensive phone calls from home. The consequence would be a large bill for their parents or guardians. The rule would be 'Ask permission before making phone calls.' The students should complete the chart, listing an action, its consequence to others and a subsequent rule.

Plenary

Draw out that rules and laws are intended to protect people, their property, public property, animals and the environment.

Rules for reasons

☞ Which of the rules are good and which are not?
Put a tick or a cross in each box.

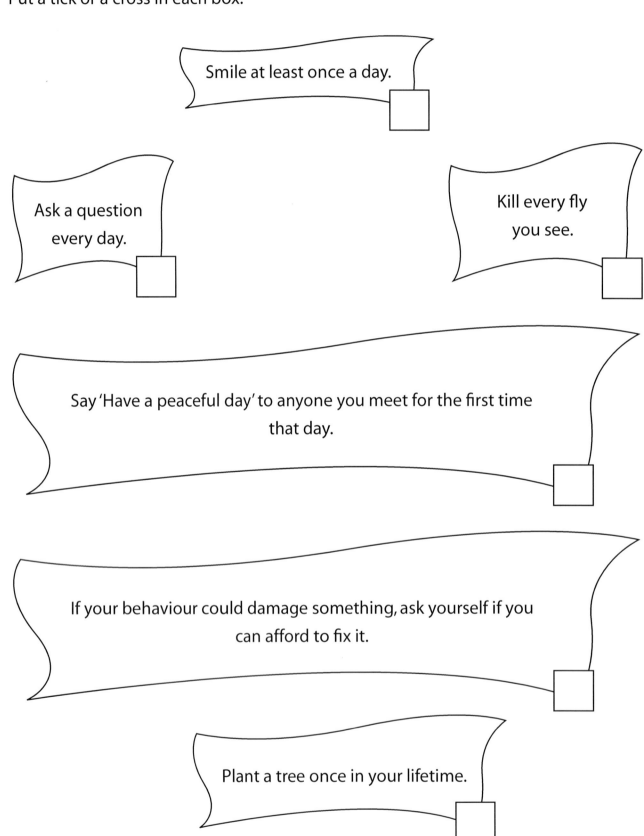

Smile at least once a day.

Ask a question every day.

Kill every fly you see.

Say 'Have a peaceful day' to anyone you meet for the first time that day.

If your behaviour could damage something, ask yourself if you can afford to fix it.

Plant a tree once in your lifetime.

RE Ethics and moral issues

Activity sheet – Rules and laws

Your rules

☞ Discuss these situations with a partner.

What would you do?

Complete the chart. Your actions show that you follow rules, even though you might not think about them. Write the rules.

Situation	What I would do	Rule
Your friend says he cannot come out with you and the others. He doesn't say why but you know that he has no pocket money because his dad has lost his job.		
One of your friends has been arrested for theft from a local shop.		
You and your friends plan to spend a day at the beach. You find out that one friend's grandmother has died.		

Lawbreakers

☞ What harm have these lawbreakers done to others? Are their punishments fair?
Make notes on a separate piece of paper.

Callum is 13.
He has been found guilty of shoplifting and has been banned from all shops unless he is with an adult.

Leona is 15.
She has an Anti-Social Behaviour Order and is not allowed out after 7:00pm because she damaged several neighbours' cars.

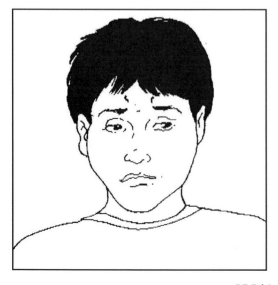

Jack is 16.
He has been fined for being drunk and disorderly in the town centre.

Religious laws

It is a crime to disobey the laws of the land.

It is not always a crime to disobey a religious law.

☞ List some religious laws which are not connected with crime.

Law	Religion it belongs to	Reason for the law, if you know it

☞ Choose a religious law you do not know the reason for.

_____

Find out why this religion has this law.

Write notes on a separate piece of paper. Use them to help you to write a report.

Activity sheet – Rules and laws

Lawmakers

Your actions affect the people around you. They can also affect people further away. They can even affect people a long way away.

👉 In each box, list three common actions which affect others in a bad way. Write rules about them.

Where	Action			Consequence to others	Rule
At home					
At school					
In the local community					

RE Ethics and moral issues

Teacher's notes

Fair and unfair

Objectives

- Know about some ways in which religious beliefs affect people's actions
- Know about some ways in which scriptures affect the lives of believers

Prior knowledge

The students should show some knowledge about the beliefs of Buddhists, Christians, Hindus, Jews, Muslims and Sikhs.

QCA link

Unit 8C Beliefs and practice

Scottish attainment targets

Personal search
Strand – Relationships and moral values
Level E

Background

There are charities linked with most religions. Examples of religious-based charities which help children in need include Islamic Relief (www.islamic-relief.com/uk/welcome/welcome_screen.html), Muslim Aid (www.muslimaid.org), Christian Aid (www.christian-aid.org.uk), CAFOD (www.cafod.org.uk), Khalsa Aid (www.afghanhindu.info/khalsaaid.htm), SEWA International (www.sewainternational.com) and Norbu Charitable Foundation (www.ncf.net).

Starter activity

Copy activity sheet 'Yours by right' onto an OHT and invite volunteers to read the list of children's rights. These are simplified from The Rights of the Child, agreed by UNICEF in 1989. Ask the students why they think it was necessary for the convention of The Rights of the Child to be drawn up. Point out the date when it was drawn up. Do all or most children have these rights? What difference has the charter made?

Activity sheets

'Yours by right'. Cut a copy of the activity sheet into separate cards and give each pair of students one card (numbers 1–10) to discuss. Ask them to list examples of what each means in practice. Encourage them to think of examples relating to their local community as well as for children in other localities.

'Lost rights'. Ask the students to read the newspaper reports and then to read the Rights of the Child (see 'Yours by right'). They should be able to identify one or more rights denied to the children in each newspaper report which they can then match to one of the Rights of the Child.

'Charities for children'. Ask the students if they know of any organisations which help children who are denied their rights. Ask different groups to find out about the work of different religious charities which help children. They could use the Internet (see Background), but also help them to find out about the work of religions in their local community. If possible, arrange visits to places of worship to find out about their charitable work. The students could also look out for charitable appeals in local newspapers, collection boxes in local shops and so on, and to find out about those which help children. Afterwards, each group could make a short presentation to the others about what they have found out, including examples of the difference the charity's work is making to the lives of children.

'A fair world' encourages the students to consider the meaning of a 'fair world'. Does this mean that everyone should have exactly the same in terms of health, water, food, education and so on? Discuss the reality that people are born into families which have different homes, localities, incomes and so on, and draw out the idea of equality of opportunity. The students should complete the chart.

Plenary

Ask the students what they think individuals can do to help children in a specific locality or situation to have their rights upheld.

Yours by right

1 You have all these rights.

2 To grow up in a healthy and normal way, free and with dignity.

3 To have a name and to be a member of a country.

4 Protection, good food, a home and medical care.

5 Special care if disabled in any way.

6 Love and understanding, from parents and family if possible, otherwise from the government.

7 Free school, play and equal opportunities.

8 Education and guidance from parents.

9 Always to be among the first to get help and protection from cruelty or exploitation. Not to work before a minimum age and never when it would harm your health or moral and physical development.

10 To be taught peace, understanding, tolerance and friendship among all people.

Activity sheet – Fair and unfair

Lost rights

☞ Which rights are these children not being given?
Match each report to one of the Rights of the Child on 'Yours by right'.

Baby dies after raw food diet

Six-month-old Gemma died weighing only seven pounds after being fed only wheat grass, coconut water and almond milk. Her parents believe in a diet of uncooked foods.

No hospital treatment for burned toddler

Susan Jones, 34, was arrested after it was found that she did not take her one-year-old son to the hospital after he received second-degree burns from a hot frying pan. The toddler's burns are now being treated and he is doing well.

Children in cotton fields

Narasamma, 12, has worked in the cotton fields for the last five years. She sleeps in a cattle shed and works more than 13 hours a day, with two breaks.

Too poor for school

Amara had to leave school at the age of eight because her father did not earn enough to support the whole family. She started working in a clothing factory to help.

Children beaten by father

Leah and her sister would hide when they heard their father coming home drunk. They knew he would beat their mother and then start on them.

Orphaned at five

When Sara's parents died, she went to live with her grandmother, a basket weaver. She started work young, helping her grandmother with housework, cooking and basket weaving. She went to school but often she had to miss classes to travel miles to sell their baskets. When she was ten, she had to leave school altogether to help her grandmother with her work.

Activity sheet – Fair and unfair

Charities for children

☞ Find out how a religious charity is helping to give children their rights.
Make notes on the chart.

Use your notes to help you to present a report to your group.

Name of charity:	Religion:
Address:	Phone number: Website: Email:
Aim or mission statement:	How it raises funds:
How it puts its aim into practice:	
Recent achievement:	

RE Ethics and moral issues © Folens (copiable page)

Activity sheet – Fair and unfair

A fair world

☞ Do you think everyone in the world should have exactly the same?

Think about:

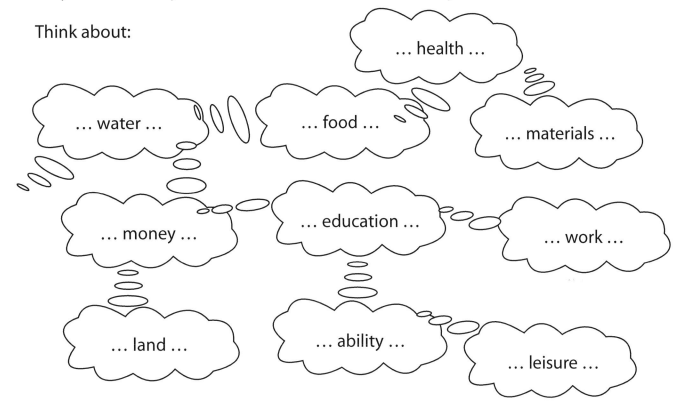

Make notes to help you to present an argument about this.

For	Against
I think everyone should have exactly the same because…	I do not think everyone should have exactly the same because…
1.	1.
2.	2.
3.	3.
4.	4.
Conclusion If everyone had exactly the same…	Conclusion If everyone did not have exactly the same…

RE Ethics and moral issues

Teacher's notes

Justice

Objectives

- Recount stories about Christian leaders
- Identify and consider basic questions and ideas about who is a leader and what it means to be a follower

Prior knowledge

The students should show awareness of ways in which religious people try to serve others and how choices in life may relate to beliefs about God and humanity. They should be given opportunities to develop skills of empathy, reflection and application in RE.

QCA links

Units 7B What does justice mean for Christians? and 8C Beliefs and practice

Scottish attainment targets

Personal search
Strand – Relationships and moral values
Level E

Background

The students can find out more about the Scottish legal system from www.bbc.co.uk/crime/fighters/scotssheriffcourts.shtml and the legal system in England, Wales and Northern Ireland from www.bbc.co.uk/crime/law/englandcourts.shtml. In England, the Magistrates' Court is where people first appear when they have been charged with a criminal offence. Also, some 'summary only' offences, for example, common assault, can only be tried there. In Scotland, the equivalent is the Sheriff Court. The story 'Three men and an angel' is from the Hadiths (stories from and about the Prophet Muhammad pbuh).

Starter activity

Read a newspaper report about a crime for which someone has been punished, for example, robbery or vandalism. Ask the students if justice was done. Encourage them to explain their answers. Should the same punishment be given to anyone who commits the same crime? Is punishment necessary for justice to be done? Ask them how they would feel if they or their families had been the victims. Would they forgive the culprits? Would they want revenge? Make a note of their responses.

Activity sheets

'The boy who stole the recorder'. Ask the students to read the story with a partner or in a group. Invite feedback. Was justice done? Ask them what justice means. Is this justice for the person who did wrong, for the victims, or for both?

'Your justice'. Provide some newspaper stories about crimes but cut out and keep the reports of the sentences passed on the offenders. Ask the students, in pairs, to consider how offenders deserve to be treated. For whose benefit are offenders punished? Is this justice? What is its purpose? Compare their suggested treatments of the offenders with what actually happened.

'Three men and an angel' and 'Fair deal' are to be used together. Explain to the students that the story is from Islam and ask them to read it or to follow it while you read it aloud. Does this story show justice? Ask them to explain their answers. Discuss whether people usually get what they deserve. Encourage the students to talk about examples they know to support or oppose this. They should consider each part of the story in turn. Is each part just or unjust? Read the example with them and explain that this is the type of summary they should write. Discuss their answers. Was the situation at the start just and fair? How might this have affected what the three men did? Why did one of them respond differently from the others when the angels returned?

'A just God?' is based on a true story in which a mother forgave her son's murderers. Ask the students to complete this activity sheet without discussion. They should concentrate on the meaning of justice and how it was put into practice in this story. How did the Walker family's Christian faith influence their actions? Were the students surprised at their response? Why? Discuss how common this type of response is and the difference it would make if it were more common. How is forgiveness practised in other religions? The students could find out about forgiveness in other religions.

Plenary

Review the students' responses to the Starter activity. What were their views about justice? Ask them if their views have changed in any way during the course of these activities and, if so, how.

The boy who stole a recorder

The defendant was 16 years old. He had admitted that he had broken into a school. The only thing he had stolen was a recorder. Now the Sheriff* had to pass sentence. Why had the boy chosen a recorder to steal?

'Did you learn to play the recorder at school?' he asked the youngster.

'I learned a bit but I couldn't play it much,' answered the boy.

'Do you have a recorder now?' asked the Sheriff (the stolen one had been confiscated by the police, of course).

'No.'

'Well,' said the Sheriff, 'Your fine shall be £25, but I will defer the sentence for six months. If you buy a recorder and learn to play well enough I will fine you only £5. If you don't, I will fine you the full £25.'

Six months later the court was filled with newspaper reporters. They had never heard of this type of sentence before. The Sheriff said that the boy should not play the recorder in court but took him, with two officials and just one reporter, into a side room. The boy showed them the recorder he said he had bought.

'What tune are you going to play?' asked the Sheriff.

'Amazing Grace.'

The Sheriff listened. What he heard did not sound much like *Amazing Grace*. A 16 year old should have been able to play better than that if he had been practising for six months.

'That was not very good but you have got a recorder and you have gone some way towards learning to play it. I shall fine you £12.'

* In Scotland a Sheriff passes sentences at a Sheriff Court.
This is based on a true story told in *In and Out of Court* by Sheriff Nigel Thomson of Edinburgh.

☞ Was justice done?

Discuss your answer and make notes on a separate piece of paper.

Your justice

☞ Work with a partner.

Read two newspaper reports about crimes.

Do not read about any sentences passed on culprits who were found guilty.

Discuss what sentences should be passed on the culprits.

Think about:

... fines ...

... help ...

... jail ...

... supervision ...

... work ...

... tasks ...

Write notes on the chart.

Summary of the crime	Sentence	Reason

Three men and an angel

An angel asked a leper what he would most value in himself. 'Good, healthy skin, because people avoid me,' he said. The angel touched him and his skin became healthy. 'What kind of property do you like?' He replied, 'Camels.' The angel gave him a pregnant camel; 'May Allah bless you in it.'

The angel asked a bald man what he would most value in himself. 'Good hair, for people mock me,' he said. The angel touched him and his hair grew. 'What kind of property do you like?' He replied, 'Cows.' The angel gave him a pregnant cow; 'May Allah bless you in it.'

The angel asked a blind man what he would most value in himself. 'Sight, so that I may see people,' he said. The angel touched his eyes and he could see: 'What kind of property do you like?' He replied, 'Sheep.' The angel gave him a pregnant ewe; 'May Allah bless you in it.'

The three animals gave birth to young. They multiplied and filled the valleys. Then the angel, disguised as a leper, went to the man who was once a leper and said, 'I am on a journey. I have nothing. In the name of Allah, who has given you such healthy skin and so much property, give me a camel.'

The man replied, 'I cannot afford to give anything.' The angel said, 'Were you not a leper? Were you not poor before Allah gave you all this property?'

He replied, 'No. I got this property from my family.' The angel said, 'If you are lying, let Allah make you as you were before.'

Then the angel, disguised as a bald man, went to the man who was once bald and said, 'I am on a journey. I have nothing. In the name of Allah, who has given you such good hair and so much property, give me a cow.'

The man replied, 'I cannot afford to give anything.' The angel said, 'Were you not bald? Were you not poor before Allah gave you all this property?'

He replied, 'No. I got this property from my family.' The angel said, 'If you are lying, let Allah make you as you were before.'

The angel, disguised as a blind man, went to the man who was once blind and said, 'I am on a journey. I have nothing. In the name of Allah who has given you sight, give me a sheep.' The man said, 'Yes, I was blind and Allah gave me sight. I was poor and Allah made me rich. So take anything you like, in Allah's name.'

The angel replied, 'Keep your property. You have been tested; Allah is pleased with you but is displeased with your two companions.'

☞ Does this story show justice?

Complete the chart on 'Fair deal'.

Fair deal

☞ Work with a partner.

Discuss the story of the leper, the blind man and the bald man in 'Three men and an angel'.

Complete the chart.

> The first summary has been done for you as an example.

Summary	Just or unjust	Reason
At the beginning of the story… ★■❄ ○❀■ ❄❀❄ ●❄□□▲✌ □■❄ ◗❀▲ ✿○●❄■❄✌ □■❄ ◗❀▲ ✿❀●❄		
Something happened…		
Then…		

RE Ethics and moral issues

Activity sheet – Justice

A just God?

Murderers sentenced

Eighteen-year-old Anthony Walker was murdered in July 2005. Paul Taylor, aged 20, admitted driving an ice axe into Anthony's head. He was sentenced to serve at least 23 years and eight months of a life sentence. Taylor's 17-year-old cousin, Michael Barton, must serve 17 years and eight months.

Anthony's mother, Gee Walker.

Do I forgive them? At the point of death, Jesus said, 'I forgive them because they do not know what they do.' I have got to forgive them. I still forgive them.

Anthony's sister, Dominique Walker.

I didn't have to think about it. It was natural to forgive. It is what our mother has always taught us.

☞ Work with a partner.

What justice is there in this story?

_____

_____

_____

What injustice is there?

_____

_____

_____

Teacher's notes

Leadership

Objectives

- Reflect on what makes some people become role-models for others and the qualities they admire in others
- Identify some qualities which make people good role-models
- Consider how leaders influence others and how to distinguish between good and bad influences
- Know about the time when a religious leader lived, about the person's beliefs and teachings
- Make informed responses to other people's values and commitments

Prior knowledge

The students should use sources of information to find out about people from the past or those who are still alive. They should have knowledge about at least two religious leaders. Students should be given opportunities to develop skills of interpretation and reflection.

QCA link

Unit 7C Religious figure

Scottish attainment targets

Other world religions
Strand – Sacred writings, stories and key figures
Level C;
Strand – Beliefs
Level D

Background

Guru Nanak was born to a Hindu family in 1469 in Talwandi, near Lahore. In about 1496, he disappeared from sight while bathing in a river. His family and friends searched, but there was no trace of him. He reappeared a few days later having been in communion with God. This is referred to as his enlightenment, after which he strove to convince people that all were equal and that whatever their religion they worshipped the same god. He founded the Sikh religion. He died in 1539, having named Guru Angad as his successor.

Mohandas Gandhi (given the name 'Mahatma' meaning 'great soul') was born in 1869 to Hindu parents in the state of Gujarat in Western India. After studying in London, he became a lawyer and went to work in South Africa, where he became committed to improving the rights of immigrant Indians and developed his creed of passive resistance against injustice. His lobbying eventually led to the independence of India from Britain in 1947. He was assassinated in 1948.

Starter activity

Show photographs of well-known people: politicians, sportspeople, film stars, musicians, modern religious leaders. As you show each one, ask the students if each figure influences them in any way. On the flip chart, record the number of students each person influences. Who has the most influence on the class? Discuss why.

Activity sheets

'Copycats' follows on from the Starter activity. Ask the students, in pairs, to discuss well-known people and to consider how they influence others. They should complete the table and then separate the influences into lists of good and bad.

'Role-model'. Ask the students to think about their role-model. What makes them admire this person and want to emulate him or her? Invite feedback. Are the students impressed by fashion, wealth, talent or personal qualities?

'Guru Nanak' and 'Mohandas Ghandi'. Discuss what is meant by 'personal qualities' and ask the students to list some, for example, commitment, fairness, generosity, honesty, loyalty and patience. Ask them to read the passages about Guru Nanak and Mohandas Ghandi. They should discuss and make notes about the qualities they have.

'A good leader'. Ask the students to think about what 'a good leader' means. They should complete the chart. Draw out that leadership does not mean being able to force or trick people into a course of action but in convincing them that it is right.

'Set an example'. Ask the students if they are influenced by older students. In what ways? Discuss good and bad influences. Ask them whether older students have a responsibility to consider their influence on younger students. The students should plan an argument to support their answer.

Plenary

Ask the students what they have learned about influencing others and about the qualities of a good leader.

Activity sheet – Leadership

Copycats

☞ How do well-known people influence what others do?

Discuss this with a partner.

List your ideas on the chart.

Person's name	How he or she influences others				
	Beliefs	Clothes	Choice of career	Leisure activities	Other

☞ Which of these influences are good and which are bad?
Make two lists on a separate piece of paper.

☞ What makes people follow bad influences?
Make notes on a separate piece of paper.

Role-model

☞ Who would be your role-model, and why?

_____

Complete the table.

Role-model's good qualities	Actions showing these qualities

☞ What have you done which has been influenced by your role-model?

_____

_____

_____

What else could you do?

_____

_____

_____

RE Ethics and moral issues

Activity sheet – Leadership

Guru Nanak

☞ Read the passages about Guru Nanak, the first Sikh guru.
What qualities or skills do his actions or words show?
Write in the boxes and link to the key words and phrases.

Guru Nanak saw some pilgrims in the holy River Ganges. They were throwing water towards the Sun. He asked, 'Why do you throw water like that?' They said they were offering it to their ancestors. Guru Nanak started throwing water in the opposite direction. They asked what he was doing. 'I am sending water to my farm which is dry,' he said. 'But water cannot reach your crops so far away,' they said. Guru Nanak replied, 'If your water can reach your ancestors near the Sun, mine can reach my fields a short distance away.'

Guru Nanak stopped at Saidpur in Western Punjab. The first Mughal Emperor, Babar, had invaded the region. The guru's friend, Mardana, asked Guru Nanak why so many innocent people were killed along with the few who were guilty. Guru Nanak told Mardana to wait under a banyan tree and that he would come back to answer the question. While sitting under the tree, Mardana was bitten by an ant. He angrily stamped on as many ants as he could. Guru Nanak came back and said, 'Now you know Mardana, why the innocent suffer along with the guilty.'

Mohandas Gandhi

☞ Read what some people who met Mohandas Gandhi wrote about him.

What qualities did he have?

Write in the boxes and link to the key words and phrases.

> Joseph Doke wrote, in 1909, in his biography of Gandhi:
>
> 'There was a quiet, assured strength about him, a greatness of heart, a transparent honesty, that attracted me at once.'
>
> 'He lives on a higher plane than most men do … Those who do not know him, think there is some unworthy motive behind it to account for such profound unworldliness. But those who know him well are ashamed of themselves in his presence…'
>
> 'Money I think has no charm for him. His compatriots are angry. They say, "He will take nothing. The money we gave him when he went as our deputy to England he brought back to us again. The presents we made him in Natal, he handed over to our public funds."'
>
> 'They wonder at him, grow angry at his strange unselfishness, and love him with the love of pride and trust.'

> Professor Gilbert Murray wrote that people 'should be careful how they deal with a man who cares nothing for sensual pleasure, nothing for riches, nothing for comfort or praise or promotion, but is simply determined to do what he believes to be right.'

☞ In what ways was Mohandas Gandhi different from most people?

Make notes on a separate piece of paper.

Activity sheet – Leadership

A good leader

☞ What makes a good leader?
Complete the table.

Statement	True or false	Reason
A good leader needs a lot of money.		
A good leader needs to have a powerful group of followers.		
A good leader sets an example for others to follow.		
A good leader must be honest.		
A good leader must be wise.		
A good leader must be famous.		
A good leader is always a man.		
A good leader must be able to explain ideas simply.		
A good leader must be religious.		
A good leader has to have clear goals.		
A good leader must dress well.		
A good leader needs a loud voice.		

Set an example

☞ Do you think older students at a school have a responsibility to set an example for the younger ones?

Plan an argument to support your answer.

Introduction:	
Why older students should set an example:	**Evidence:**
Why older students should not have to set an example:	**Evidence:**
Conclusion: Older students should/should not have to set an example for younger ones because…	

Teacher's notes

One Earth

Objectives

- State an opinion about an environmental issue but recognise that others might hold a different view
- Reflect on ultimate questions about the environment and about the purpose of the world

Prior knowledge

The students should be given opportunities to consider the responsibilities people have towards the environment and the ethical questions concerning the connections between environmental concerns and economic progress.

QCA link

Unit 7E What are we doing to the environment?

Scottish attainment targets

Personal search
Strand – The natural world
Level D

Background

The DEFRA (Department of Food and Rural Affairs) website gives factual information about global warming, including the amounts of carbon dioxide released into the atmosphere during different eras (and the sources), how this affects the environment and how humans are changing the environment in other ways: www.defra.gov.uk/environment/climatechange/schools/links/index.htm. See also Environment Agency: www.environment-agency.gov.uk/, RSPB (Royal Society for the Protection of Birds): www.rspb.org.uk/, Greenpeace: www.greenpeace.org/international/, Mammal Society: www.abdn.ac.uk/mammal/ and Endangered Species: www.endangeredspecie.com/.

Starter activity

Show the students photographs of flooding in Asia and in the UK. Identify the location of each picture and ask the students if the scene worries them. Point out that flooding is becoming more common in some areas because sea levels and the level of the water table are rising. Do they know what scientists think is the main cause? Ask them if they know what global warming means and if they know any factors which are thought to cause it.

Activity sheets

'A sad Earth' and 'A happier Earth'. Ask volunteers to read the statements on 'A sad Earth'. Have they heard them before? Ask if any are new to them. If all these are well-known effects of human actions, why do people continue to do them? Does knowledge of the consequences always change human behaviour? Ask the students to suggest why not. List the factors which contribute to this, for example, time, cost and commitment. Ask them to discuss with a partner what could be done and to complete 'A happier Earth'.

'Earth sense'. Ask the students to agree on the answers before they write them. Invite feedback. Which items are the responsibility of everyone? Draw out that we all have a responsibility towards all of them. The students should find out about an organisation that helps to protect one of the items.

'Who cares?' Ask the students to decide which statements are reasonable and which are not. Are some reasonable for some people but not for others? Why? Invite feedback. Encourage students to justify their answers.

'Your issue.' Ask the students about the environmental issues which interest them. Ask if they think these issues are relevant to their local community. Help them to plan and carry out a survey to find out about the extent to which this particular environmental damage is perpetuated locally. The students could question their families and neighbours.

Plenary

Help the students to summarise what they have learned by asking questions such as *Are people harming the Earth? How? If they learn about the consequences, do they continue with behaviour which harms the environment? Do they care about the environment? What stops them taking care of it?* Discuss how this information can inform policies for improvement. Ask why we should take care of the Earth. Why does it matter?

A sad Earth

☞ Read these statements and complete 'A happier Earth'.

1. More and more carbon dioxide is released into the atmosphere through industry.

2. Motor vehicles release carbon monoxide and carbon dioxide into the air. There are more and more vehicles on the roads each year.

3. Goods are becoming cheaper and the cost of labour is rising; so people throw things away and buy new goods rather than having them repaired.

4. More and more homes are needed. Habitats are destroyed to make space for them.

5. Forests are known as 'sinks'; this means that they absorb carbon dioxide and give out oxygen. Forests are being cut for wood and to clear the land for growing crops, grazing animals and building homes and factories.

6. Fossil fuels such as coal and oil are burned for power and to produce electricity. This produces carbon dioxide. More and more fuel is being used to heat homes and to power electrical devices.

7. Airports are expanding because air transport is increasing. Habitats and historic sites are destroyed to make space for them.

A happier Earth

☞ Read the statements on 'A sad Earth'.

What can be done to stop each type of damage to the Earth?

Write in the boxes.

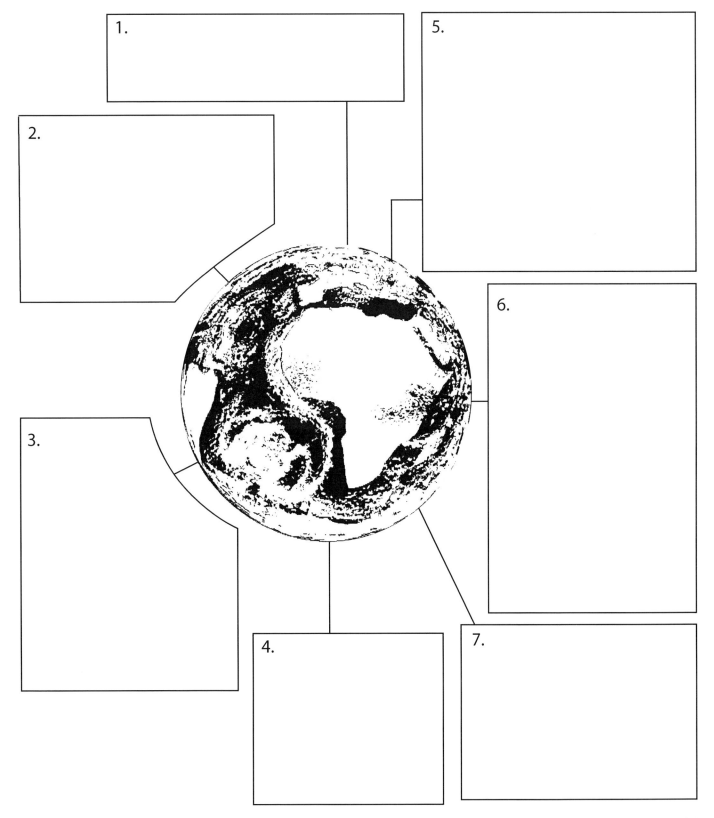

1.

2.

3.

4.

5.

6.

7.

Earth sense

☞ Work with a group.

Who do you think is responsible for looking after these?

Write in the boxes.

☞ Find out about an organisation which helps to protect one of these.

Collect pictures and make notes to give a presentation about it.

Suggest what everyone can do to help.

Activity sheet – One Earth

Who cares?

☞ Tick the statements you agree with.

People should only buy environmentally-friendly goods, even if they cost more.	
Governments should subsidise environmentally-friendly goods.	
There should be high taxes on goods which are not environmentally-friendly.	
We should recycle everything we can, even if this takes time and effort.	
Local councils should make recycling easy by separating the waste after we have put it all into one bin.	
People should be charged by the kilogram for the rubbish collected from their homes.	
We should have goods repaired rather than throwing them away, even if this costs more.	
Repairs to household goods should be subsidised by the government.	
Wages should be reduced so that labour costs are lower and people will have goods repaired rather than throwing them away when they are broken.	
There should be high taxes on new goods so that people will be more likely to have broken things repaired.	
Manufactured goods should be collected and reconditioned by the makers when they are too old to use.	
Local councils should pay for goods to be reconditioned and sold much more cheaply than new ones.	
We should not throw any goods away if they are usable, including clothes, household goods and computers.	

Activity sheet – One Earth

Your issue

☞ Think about a way in which businesses and individuals in your local area harm the Earth.

Observe and make notes. Use the boxes below to help you.

Carry out a survey to find out why they harm the Earth. Complete the table below.

Using fuel: electricity, gas, oil, petrol.	Polluting the air.	Polluting water by pouring liquids down drains.
Buying food and other goods in a great deal of packaging.	Using disposables: cups, nappies, tissues, dusters.	Using material: paper, cloth, metal, glass, plastic, wood and so on.

My issue:		
Observations		
Place	**People**	**Reasons**

RE Ethics and moral issues

Teacher's notes

Beliefs and values

Objective

● Identify some important or ultimate questions and suggest ways in which some people might try to answer them

Prior knowledge

The students should show awareness that people's beliefs are personal to them. They should also have understanding that belief in God affects people's behaviour. Students should be given opportunities to develop skills of empathy, interpretation and reflection; to debate.

QCA links

Unit 7A Where do we look for God? and *8C* Beliefs and practice

Scottish attainment targets

Personal search
Strand – Ultimate questions
Level D

Background

The story known as 'The Cottingley Fairies', about Elsie Wright and Frances Griffiths' photographs of fairies in Elsie's garden at Cottingley, near Bradford, was believed and the photographs considered authentic by many people, including Elsie's mother and Sir Arthur Conan Doyle, both of whom believed in spiritualism. Frances always maintained that the fairies were real but in 1983, five years before her death, on *Nationwide*, Elsie Wright admitted that it been a hoax. The story provides a background against which to discuss what makes different people have different beliefs about the same evidence or explanation.

Starter activity

Use 'What can you see?' to introduce the activities. Copy the optical illusion on the activity sheet onto an OHT. Show it to the students and ask them to write down what they see. Draw out that the evidence of the senses can be interpreted differently by different people.

Activity sheets

'What do you know?' The students should complete the chart individually. Allow time for them to explain each of their answers with a partner. On the flip chart, list the statements everyone agrees are true. Why are they so certain? Draw out that some of them are facts which can be looked up, observed or proved; that, in the same way, some, such as 'New York is the capital city of the USA', can be proved untrue. Explain that the truth of some depends on other factors, for example, a 100-watt bulb might be dimmer than a 40-watt bulb if the required voltage is not available.

'Believing'. Ask the students to consider their beliefs and why they hold them. Do they need proof? Can they support them with evidence? The students should complete the chart, saying whether or not they believe each statement. They should choose a statement they believe and, with a partner who also believes, try to convince another pair, who do not believe it, that it is true. Discuss whether people need evidence in order to believe in God, and that the evidence which makes some believe in God does not convince others. Draw out that some beliefs are held without evidence, and sometimes *despite* evidence which opposes them.

'Evidence'. Ask the students to read the activity sheet and to decide whether the story of the Cottingley Fairies is true. Stress that they must give reasons for their beliefs. Discuss what made some people believe it, for example, a belief in the existence of spiritual beings.

'Value'. The students should begin by judging the items according to monetary value. Help them to consider when their value could change, for example, a cow would be valuable to a family in a rural location who have few sources of food or income; a loaf of bread would be valuable to someone who is starving; clean water is essential to everyone but we might take it for granted if it is always available. Once the students have decided which items they think are valuable, they should plan an argument to convince someone who disagrees.

'Your values'. Ask the students to list what they value. To rank the items in order of value, they could consider which of them they would forego in order to keep others.

Plenary

Ask the students what they have learned through discussion about their own beliefs. Draw out the ways in which they have learned to argue about their beliefs while showing respect for other people's different beliefs.

What can you see?

☞ Write down what you can see?

_____

_____

_____

_____

RE Ethics and moral issues

Activity sheet – Beliefs and values

What do you know?

☞ Tick the statements you know are true.

☞ Take turns with a partner to show how you know a statement is true.

Liverpool is in England.	
Fugu is a type of fish.	
Ice is cold.	
New York is the capital city of America.	
A 100-watt bulb is always brighter than a 40-watt bulb.	
Henry VIII married six times.	
If you make a wish looking at the full moon, your wish will come true.	
When something burns, it gets cold.	
The sides of a square are all the same length.	
The Sun will rise tomorrow morning.	
6 + 8 = 14	
Wood floats.	
A stone will fall to the ground if you drop it.	

Believing

☞ Complete the statements by writing 'believe' or 'do not believe' in the gaps.
Explain your answer.

Statement	Reason
I _____ that the tooth fairy brings money when people have a tooth taken out.	
I _____ in magic.	
I _____ in God.	
I _____ that animals have rights.	
I _____ in ghosts.	
I _____ that people have been to the Moon.	
I _____ that there are living beings on other planets.	

☞ Choose a statement you believe very strongly.
With a partner who also believes it, find another pair who do not believe it.
Try to convince them that it is true.

RE Ethics and moral issues

Evidence

In 1917, Elsie Wright told her parents that she had seen fairies in their garden. Her parents did not believe her at first. They went to look but could see no fairies. Elsie said that the fairies did not always appear. She said she would take photographs of them to prove that they were there. This photograph shows her cousin, Frances Griffiths, with some fairies.

Some people thought the girls had faked the photograph. Others believed it was real. One of these was Sir Arthur Conan Doyle, the author of the *Sherlock Holmes* stories.

☞ What do you think?
Talk to a partner and write notes about your ideas on a separate piece of paper.

Activity sheet – Beliefs and values

Value

☞ Tick the items you think are valuable.

Share your ideas with a partner.

Put two ticks next to the ones you agree on.

☞ Chose an item you ticked.

List some reasons why it is valuable.

Plan an argument to convince someone who disagrees.

Make notes on a separate piece of paper.

RE Ethics and moral issues © Folens (copiable page)

Activity sheet – Beliefs and values

Your values

☞ List ten things you value.

Think about…

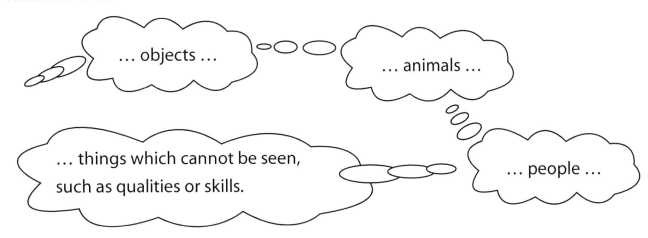

… objects …

… animals …

… things which cannot be seen, such as qualities or skills.

… people …

Write notes on the notepad, then, when you have made a final decision, list them in order with the most important at the top.

Valued top ten

1 _____

2 _____

3 _____

4 _____

5 _____

6 _____

7 _____

8 _____

9 _____

10 _____

Teacher's notes

Humans and the universe

Objectives

- Make comparisons between religion and science
- Select relevant information from written sources to produce coherent answers to questions on the purpose of human life and reflect on their own understanding about it

Prior knowledge

The students should know how people's religion affects their views of the world. They should also take into account scientific understanding when discussing religious teaching. Students should be given opportunities to explore concepts of meaning and to develop skills of empathy, interpretation and reflection and to agree and disagree with others in a constructive way.

QCA link

Unit 9B Where did the universe come from?

Scottish attainment targets

Personal search
Strand – The natural world
Level D

Background

The latest figures for the population of the world can be found on www.census.gov/ipc/www/popclockworld. html and www.census.gov/ipc/www/world.html. For national and local population figures, see www. statistics.gov.uk/census/.

Starter activity

Show the students a bucket of sand. Ask each student to pick out one grain of sand. How important is that grain? Pour all the sand out of the bucket. Show them the empty bucket and ask how important each grain was.

Activity sheets

'A place in space'. Ask the students to read the information panel. How does it make them feel about the Earth? Ask if they think the Earth is an important part of the Universe. To whom? Draw out that it is important to us because we live there and depend on the Earth for our survival. Do they think there are living beings on other planets in the Universe? Is the Earth important to these beings?

'VIPs'. Ask the students to think about their own importance. If necessary, explain the meaning of context and discuss how the context affects the importance of a person. Are some people more important than others? Ask the students what is meant by 'important' and why some people might be more important than others. Is this because they are important to a greater number of people? Are they important because of what they can do, or what they can do for others? Ask how people who believe in God might view the importance of humans (to other humans and to God). This could be linked with the Christian and Jewish views that everyone is important to God, the Sikh view that we are all equal or the Muslim view that God sees all and knows all.

'I'm unique!' Draw out that in the context of the world or the universe, individual people are insignificant. Ask the students to guess the answers to the questions on the activity sheet. They can look up the answer to the first question which will then help them to answer the rest. Invite feedback and draw out that although each individual seems insignificant in a large context, everyone is a unique individual. Remind them of the bucket of sand and the importance of each grain. What does this make them think about the importance of each person?

'What are we for?' Ask the students to write what each item is for after they have discussed them with their groups. Invite feedback. On which do they all agree? Which ones did they find more difficult? Discuss whether a religious belief makes a difference to the answers people give to the question about what humans are for.

Plenary

Ask the students to consider their own purposes in life. What do they want to achieve?

Activity sheet – Humans and the universe

A place in space

☞ Read the information panel.

What does it make you think about the Earth?

Discuss in a group and make notes on a separate piece of paper.

On 6 January 2006, the world's population was 6 525 486 603 (six thousand, five hundred and twenty-five million, four hundred and eighty-six thousand, six hundred and three.)

The Earth is 150 million kilometres from the Sun. The Sun is a star in the Milky Way galaxy. There are about 200 billion stars in the Milky Way galaxy. The Milky Way galaxy measures 100 000 light years* across. Scientists are not sure how many other galaxies there are. They estimate that there could be hundreds of billions of them.

*A light year is the distance light travels in one year – that is 9 500 000 000 000 kilometres.

Activity sheet – Humans and the universe

VIPs

☞ How important are you? It depends on the context.

Mark your importance on the table.   ✓

Context	Not at all important ———→ very important				
	5	4	3	2	1
The universe					
The Milky Way					
The solar system					
The Earth					
Europe					
Britain					
Your town					
Your school					
Your class					
Your friends					
Your family					

☞ How do people become more important in different contexts?

Copy and complete the table on a separate piece of paper.

Give well-known people a score out of five for their importance.

5	4	3	2	1

Not at all important ————————————→ very important

Name	Context										
	The universe	The Milky Way	The solar system	The Earth	Europe	Britain	Your town	Your school	Your class	Your friends	Your family

RE Ethics and moral issues

Activity sheet – Humans and the universe

I'm unique!

☞ Guess the answers to these questions.

You could look up the answer to the first question, which will help you to answer the rest.

Write on the arrows.

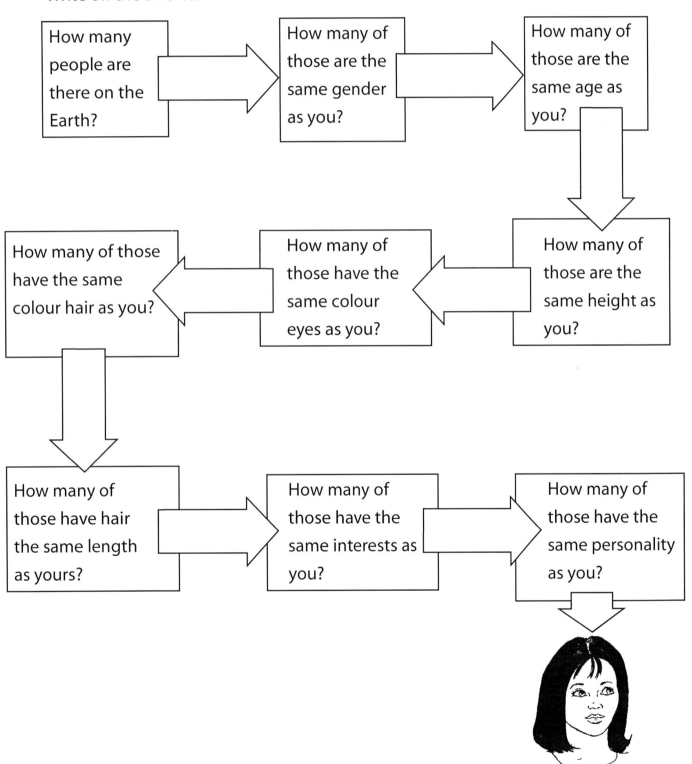

Activity sheet – Humans and the universe

What are we for?

☞ What are these for?

Discuss with your group.

Write your answers in the boxes.

RE Ethics and moral issues   © Folens (copiable page)

Teacher's notes

Rites of passage

Objectives

- Show that they know and understand some rites of passage and understand how ceremonies are important
- Make informed responses to these
- Reflect on the nature of commitment and think about their own commitments

Prior knowledge

The students should interpret source materials, taking account of different perspectives. They should be given opportunities to develop skills of empathy, interpretation and reflection and to agree and disagree with others in a constructive way.

QCA link

Unit 9A Where are we going? Rites of passage

Scottish attainment targets

Other world religions
Strand – Moral values and attitudes
Level E;
Strand – Celebration, festivals, ceremonies and customs
Level E

Background

Rites of passage have long been used in different religions and cultures to integrate biological events (birth, reproduction and death) with spiritual experience. They celebrate the connection between an individual and the community, giving meaning to that experience. Sometimes this is expressed in a non-religious way, for example, in Humanism, the birth of a baby is sometimes celebrated by a ceremony in which friends and family express their hopes for the baby and the occasion might be marked with an action such as planting a tree. A Humanist wedding or affirmation can be held anywhere, in a way which suits the couple, using words and music which are meaningful for them. This is not a legal marriage contract; the couple have to go to a Registry Office to obtain a marriage certificate, but need not exchange rings there. A Humanist funeral ceremony can take any form which is an appropriate solemn occasion to mark the death of that person and to mourn him or her; it should suit the close family. It is not hostile to religious beliefs but is a sincere way of reflecting on the reality of the life which has ended. Most include a short silent period for reflection or prayer.

Starter activity

Show a video of a *This Is Your Life* programme. Ask the students what they learned about the person whose life was featured. Draw out that it was presented mainly through the memories of other people.

Resource and activity sheets

'This is your life'. Ask the students to make a 'This Is Your Life' book about themselves. Discuss the significant occasions in their lives and how they were commemorated.

'Making commitments'. Ask the students about the age at which they think responsibility of any kind begins. After they have completed the first section of the activity sheet, invite feedback. What are the most important responsibilities everyone has? Discuss what is meant by 'commitment', including making promises and taking on new responsibilities. Draw out that, despite good intentions, it can be difficult to keep some commitments.

'Marriage or not?' Ask the students why they think people marry. Explain that in doing so they make commitments to the other person. Discuss these commitments. What can make them difficult to keep? Ask the students to write what each person would expect of the other in a marriage.

'A baby for life' could be introduced by considering how a baby is welcomed into a family and community. How do people respond to the birth of a baby? Discuss the problems which can be faced by a very young unmarried couple who have a baby. What responsibilities might they find difficult?

'The end' needs to be introduced sensitively. Ask the students what a funeral is for. Does it have to be a religious ceremony? They could find out about Humanist funerals. Ask them to complete the chart to answer what should be done when someone dies.

Plenary

Ask the students what they have learned about the purposes of religious or Humanist ceremonies for rites of passage, and why people find it important to hold ceremonies for special times in a person's life.

This is your life

☞ Make notes about your life story.

Find out about the time you cannot remember. Ask your family and other people you have known for a long time.

Use this page to help you to plan a 'This Is Your Life' book about yourself.

Event	Date	Information	Pictures or other materials to put into the book
Birth			

RE Ethics and moral issues

Making commitments

☞ List some responsibilities you have had at different ages.

Age	Responsibility
2 weeks	
1 year	
4 years	
7 years	
10 years	
13 years	

☞ If you take on a responsibility to do something, you make a commitment.

With a partner, discuss a commitment you have made recently.

What must you do to honour the commitment?

Commitment:

_____

What I must do to honour the commitment:

_____

_____

_____

_____

_____

_____

Marriage or not?

☞ With your group, discuss why couples get married.

List your ideas on the chart.

Write what would happen if they did not get married.

Reason for marriage	What would happen if the couple did not marry?

☞ Do you think it is better for couples who want to live together to marry? _____

☞ What do you think each person expects of the other in a marriage?

Write in the thought bubbles.

RE Ethics and moral issues

A baby for life

This girl is pregnant.

☞ What responsibilities will she have?
Write notes on the chart.

Baby's age	Main responsibilities
During the first weeks	
Up to 6 months	
6 months to 1 year	
1 to 3 years	
3 to 5 years	
5 to 10 years	
10 to 16 years	
16 to 18 years	
18 years onwards	

☞ How should her responsibilities be shared? With whom?
Make notes on a separate piece of paper.

The end

☞ What do you think should be done when someone dies?

What should happen to the person's body?		
Treatment ⟨ Burial, cremation or another method?	Where and how	Why
Should anything special be done?		
Special actions	Who should do them	Why
Should any special words be said?		
Special words	Who should say them	Why

RE Ethics and moral issues

Teacher's notes

Suffering

Objectives

- Give examples of different kinds of suffering
- Know a religious story about suffering and explain it in simple terms
- State their own views about suffering and relate them to religious or Humanist beliefs

Prior knowledge

The students should be able to weigh up and evaluate different responses to an issue. They should know the basic beliefs about God, people and the world.

QCA links

Unit 9A Where are we going? Rites of passage and *9C* Why do we suffer?

Scottish attainment targets

Other world religions
Strand – Moral values and attitudes
Level E

Background

According to Buddhist belief, every living being has the same basic wish – to be happy and to avoid suffering – and that we spend our lives striving to fulfil this wish. Buddhists believe that human beings spend a great deal of time and energy improving worldly conditions in their search for happiness and solutions to problems, and that the result has not been the fulfilment of their wishes but an increase in human suffering along with a decrease in happiness and peace. They believe that this indicates a need to find a true method of achieving pure happiness and freedom from misery. This comes through controlling our minds.

Starter activity

Write the word 'suffering' on the flip chart and ask the students to give some examples of suffering. Discuss what causes suffering.

Activity sheets

'Causes of suffering'. Ask the students to describe what has happened in each picture in box a and then to write what caused it in box b. Were humans to blame for any of these events?

'The Buddha'. Read the story of the Buddha aloud while the students follow it. Explain that Prince Siddhattha became known as 'the Buddha' (Enlightened One) after he had meditated and become enlightened. Explain 'enlighten', beginning with classroom examples (students become enlightened when they develop an understanding of something). Explain that the Buddha's enlightenment was about how people should live their lives. Discuss why Prince Siddhattha was so shocked at what he saw. Ask the students if they have any ideas about what he began to understand about the causes of suffering and how it can be prevented.

'The Four Noble Truths'. Copy the activity sheet onto an OHT and display it. Read the Four Noble Truths to the students and point out that these came from the Buddha's enlightenment. Read the Eightfold Path and ask the students to give examples of ways in which people who cause others to suffer might learn from it. What kinds of behaviour cause suffering?

'Stopping the suffering'. Leave the OHT of 'The Four Noble Truths' on display or give the students a copy of it. Remind them of their work on 'Causes of suffering' and ask them to refer to this as they work on 'Stopping the suffering'. Do they think human behaviour helps to cause the suffering caused by any natural disasters? How? In what ways would the Eightfold Path help to prevent it? They could also apply the Eightfold Path to suffering they read about in newspapers.

Plenary

Ask the students what they have learned about the consequences of human behaviour. Discuss any aspects of the Buddhist Eightfold Path which apply to all people, whether or not they have Buddhist beliefs.

Activity sheet – Suffering

Causes of suffering

☞ Look at the pictures below. In box a, write what has happened in each picture. In box b, write who or what could cause each of these types of suffering.

1	2
a	a
b	b
3	4
a	a
b	b

RE Ethics and moral issues © Folens (copiable page)

Activity sheet – Suffering

The Buddha

☞ Read the story of the Buddha and discuss the causes of suffering and how it could be prevented.

A prince was born in the year 623 BCE in the Lumbini grove at Kapilavatthu, in Northern India. A holy man went to see the baby. He said that one day he would be a holy man. The baby was named Siddhattha. His family name was Gotama.

To protect Prince Siddhattha from any harm from the outside world, the king did not let him out of the palace grounds. He had three palaces built for his son – one for the cold season, one for the hot season and one for the rainy season. Siddhattha had everything he needed and everything he wanted. He married Princess Yasodhara and they were very happy. They lived a life of luxury, but the prince wanted to see life outside the palaces.

He asked his servant Channa to go for a ride with him in the Lumbini grove. They came across an old man who was leaning on a stick. Every step seemed to use all his strength.

'What is wrong with him?' asked Prince Siddhattha, who had never seen anyone so old.

Channa replied, 'He is suffering because his body is old and weak. It happens to anyone who lives to a great age.'

They passed what seemed to be a bundle of rags beside the road. The bundle moved and a groan came from it. Siddhattha saw that the flesh on the arm and leg which poked out of the rags was diseased. He turned to Channa.

'She is suffering because she is ill,' he said. Siddhattha had never seen anyone ill before.

Near the river there were some people clustered around a great pile of wood. There was a body on top of the pile of wood, wrapped in a white cloth. Someone lit the wood and there was a sweet smell of sandalwood.

'Death,' said Channa. 'Suffering.'

They rode on until Siddhattha saw a man sitting cross-legged on a small mat, wearing only a piece of cloth around the lower part of his body. Siddhattha could see the outlines of bones under the man's skin. His arms and legs were so thin that they looked as if they could snap.

Siddhattha raised his puzzled eyes to Channa's face.

'He is a holy man. He hardly ever sleeps; he spends his time meditating about the meaning of life. He eats only enough to keep him alive.'

'There has to be an answer to all this suffering,' said Siddhattha, and he decided to travel all over India to find the answer.

The Four Noble Truths

During his travels, the Buddha meditated under a bodhi (banyan) tree. Eventually he began to understand the meaning of life. The answers he found were what are now known as the Four Noble Truths.

The Four Noble Truths

1   All life involves suffering.

2   Suffering comes from people wanting things.

3   Suffering stops when people stop wanting things.

4   People should follow the 'Eightfold Path'.

The Eightfold Path

1   **Right intention.** To have the right types of thoughts, to accept the Four Noble Truths and to follow the Eightfold Path.

2   **Right values.** To understand the path through which suffering will end, and reject selfishness and greed.

3   **Right speech.** To avoid saying anything hurtful and harmful.

4   **Right action.** To avoid killing and stealing, and to overcome evil with good.

5   **Right living.** To do work which benefits other people and follows the Four Noble Truths.

6   **Right effort.** To meditate in order to develop the mind, avoid doing evil and to do good deeds.

7   **Right mindedness.** To learn from the past, to be calm and not to want unnecessary things.

8   **Right meditation.** To search for enlightenment.

☞   How can people who cause others to suffer learn from the Eightfold Path? Make notes on a separate piece of paper.

Activity sheet – Suffering

Stopping the suffering

☞ Could the Eightfold Path of Buddhism prevent these types of suffering? If so, how? Write notes on the chart.

Suffering	How the Eightfold Path could prevent it

Assessment sheet

Topic _____

At the start

I knew _____

_____

I could _____

_____

Now

I have learned _____

_____

_____

_____

I can _____

_____

Next

I need to find out _____

_____

_____

I need to work on _____

_____